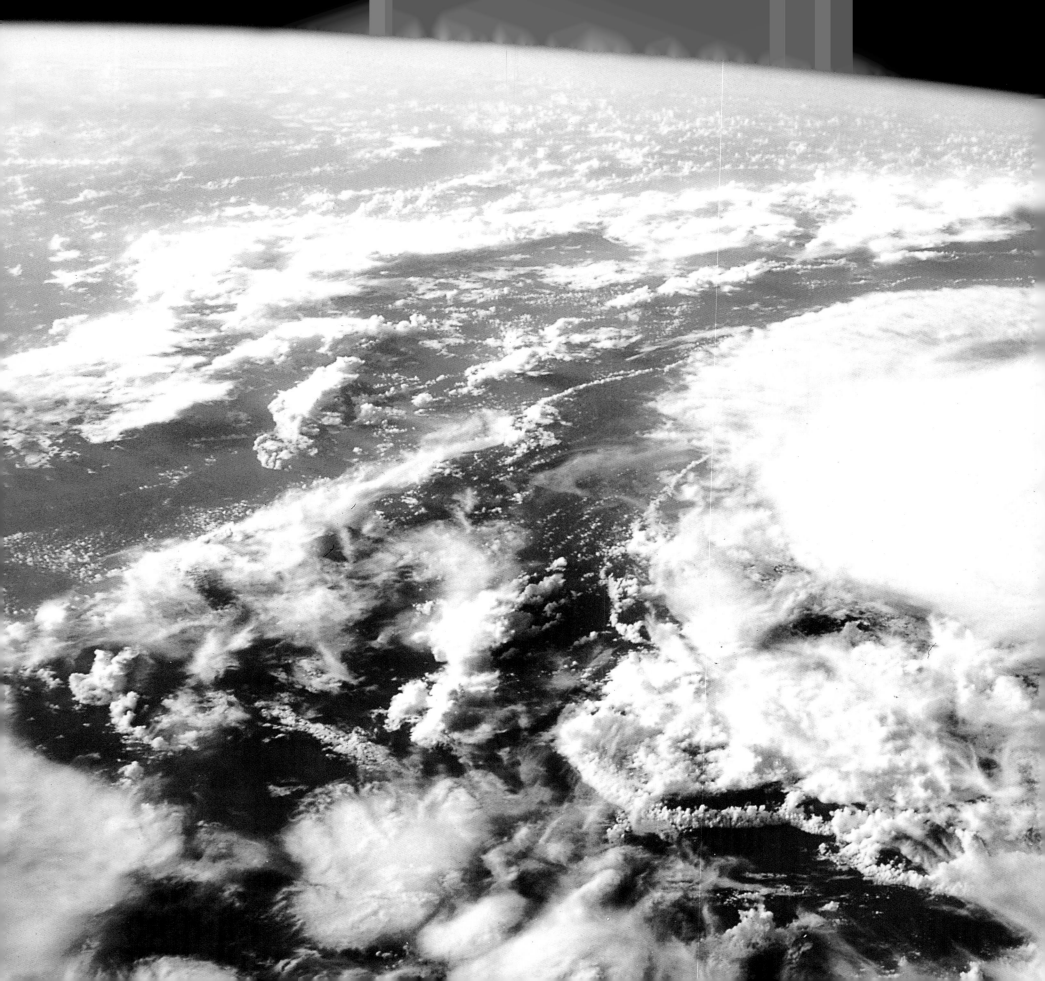

A wall of molten rock meets the sea on Hawaii's south coast, courtesy of Images Colour Library
Chris Johns

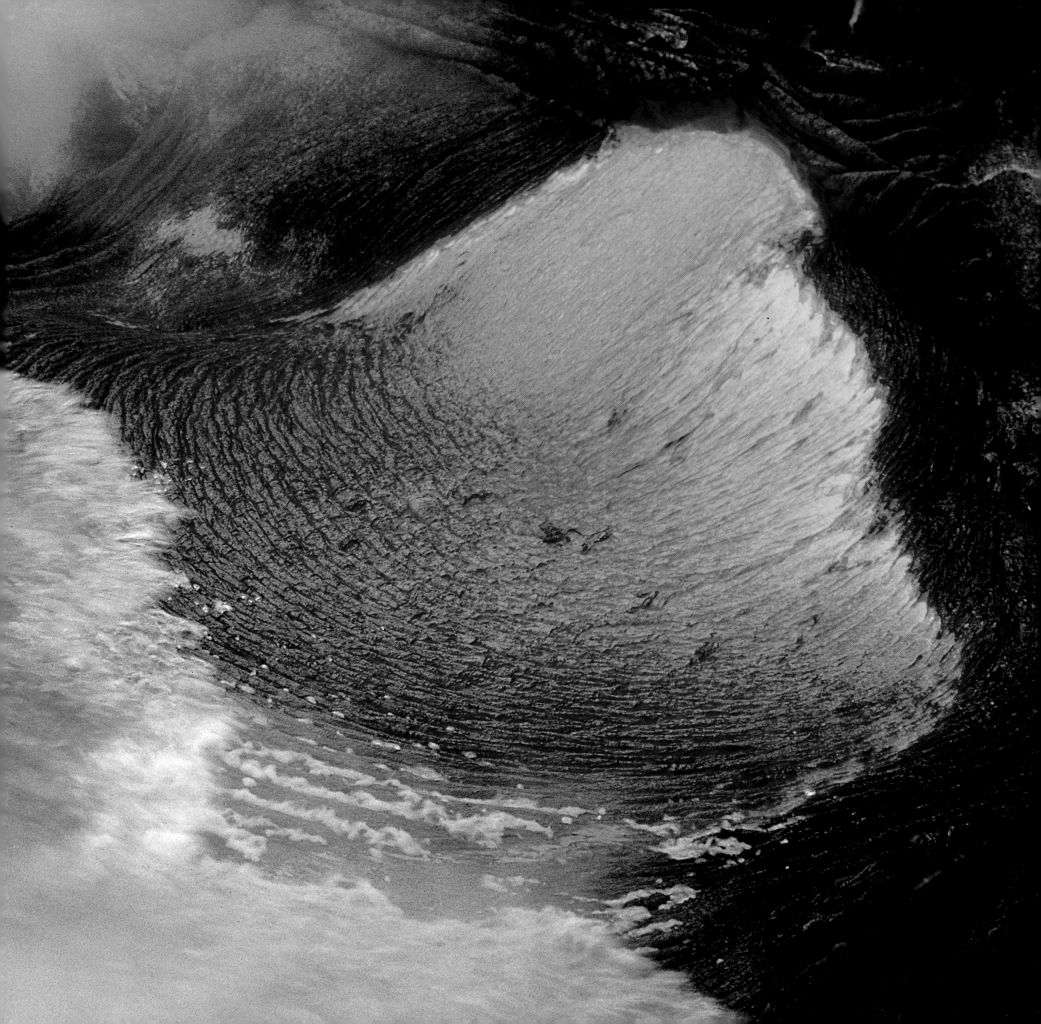

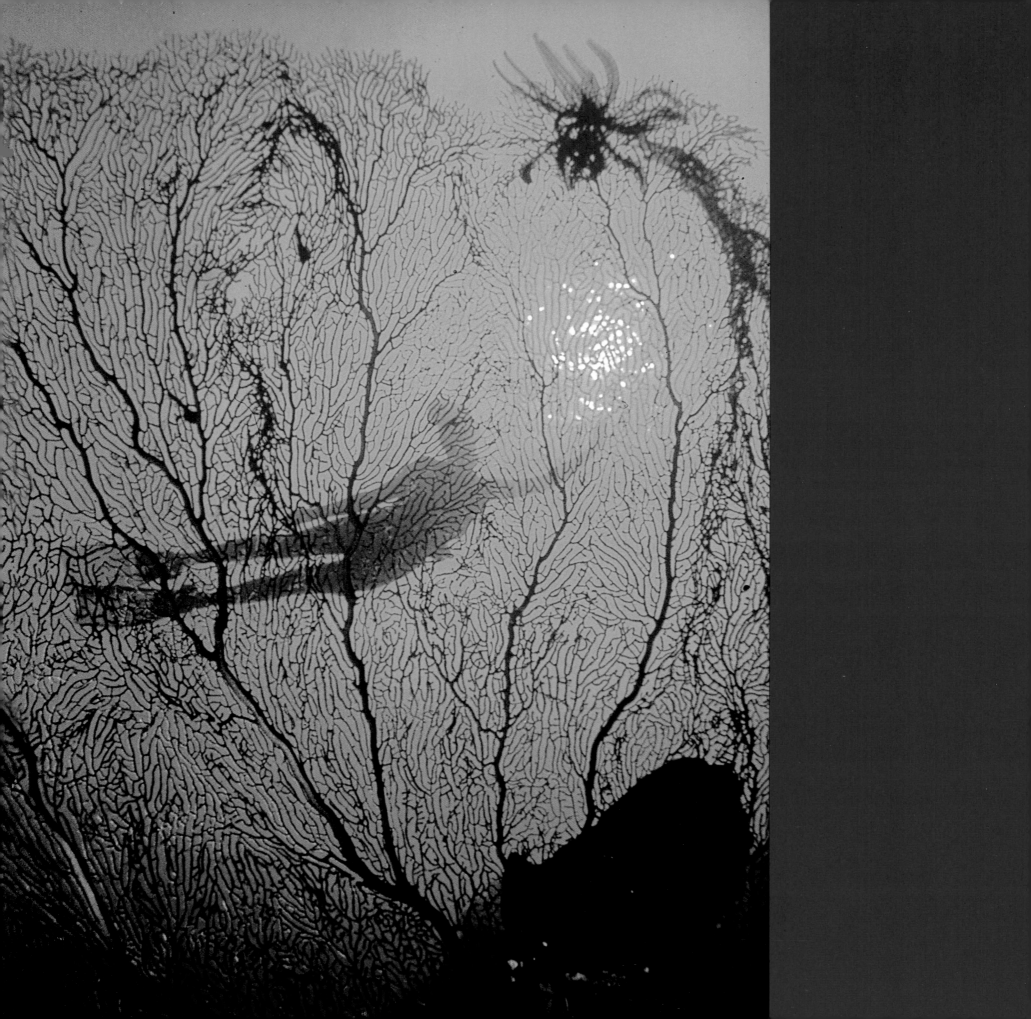

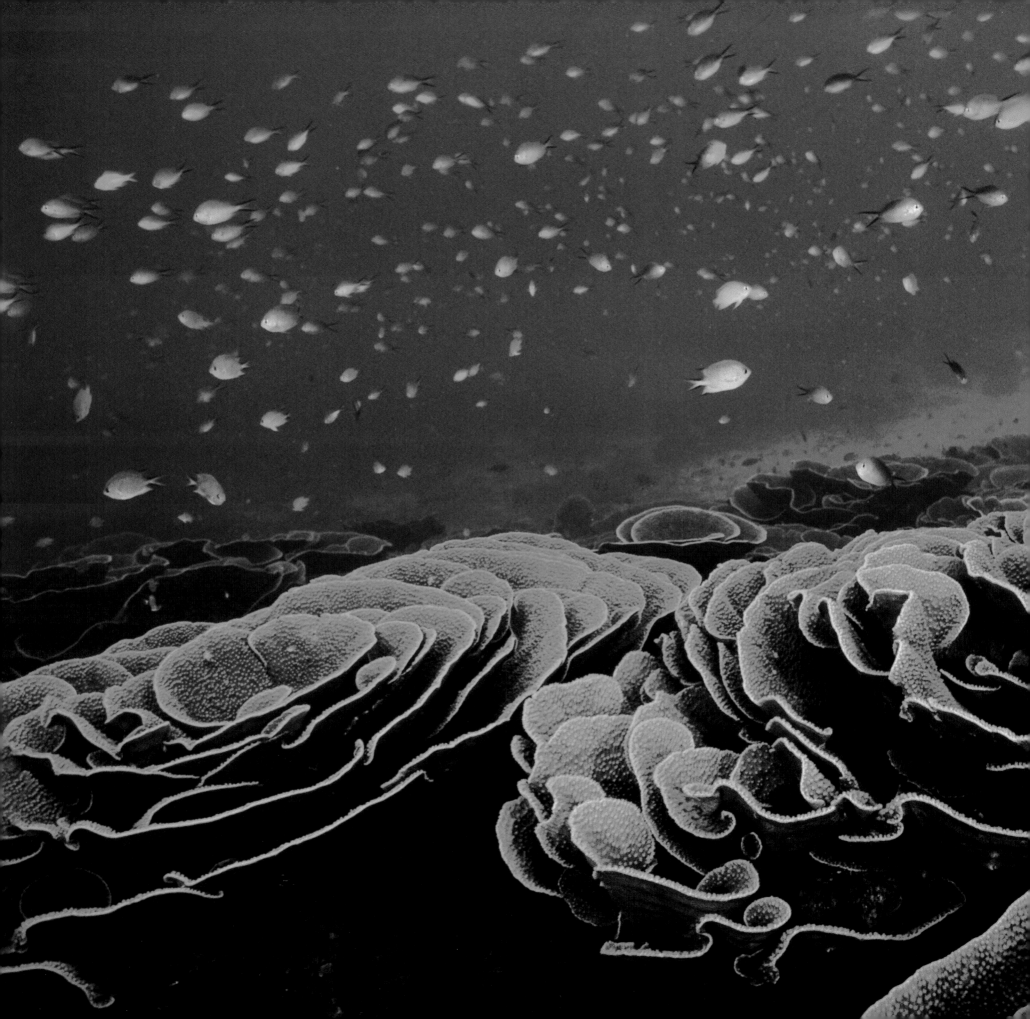

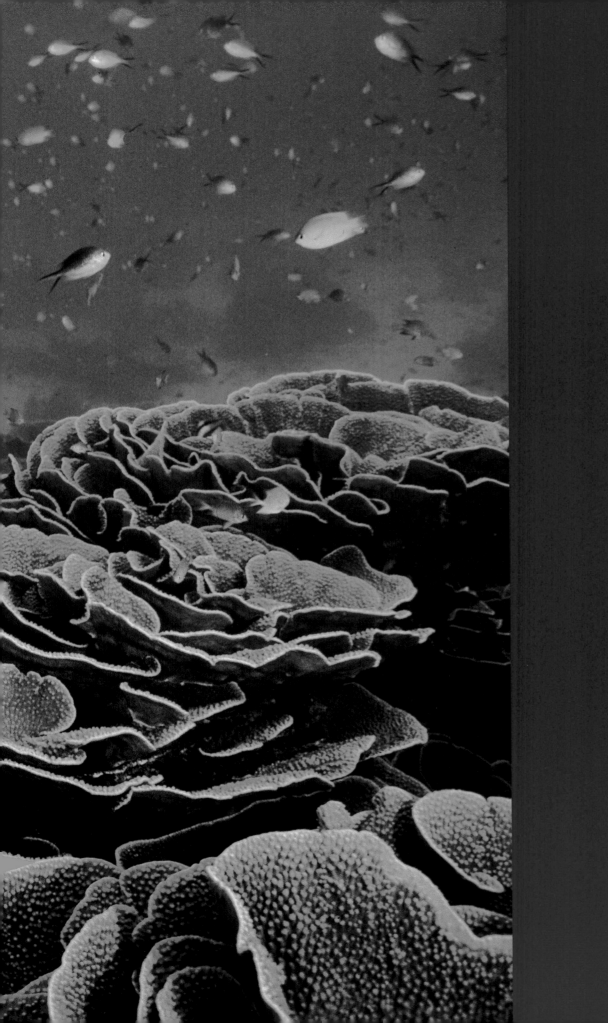

Cabbage corals
provide a home for
shoals of fish, Fiji
David Hall

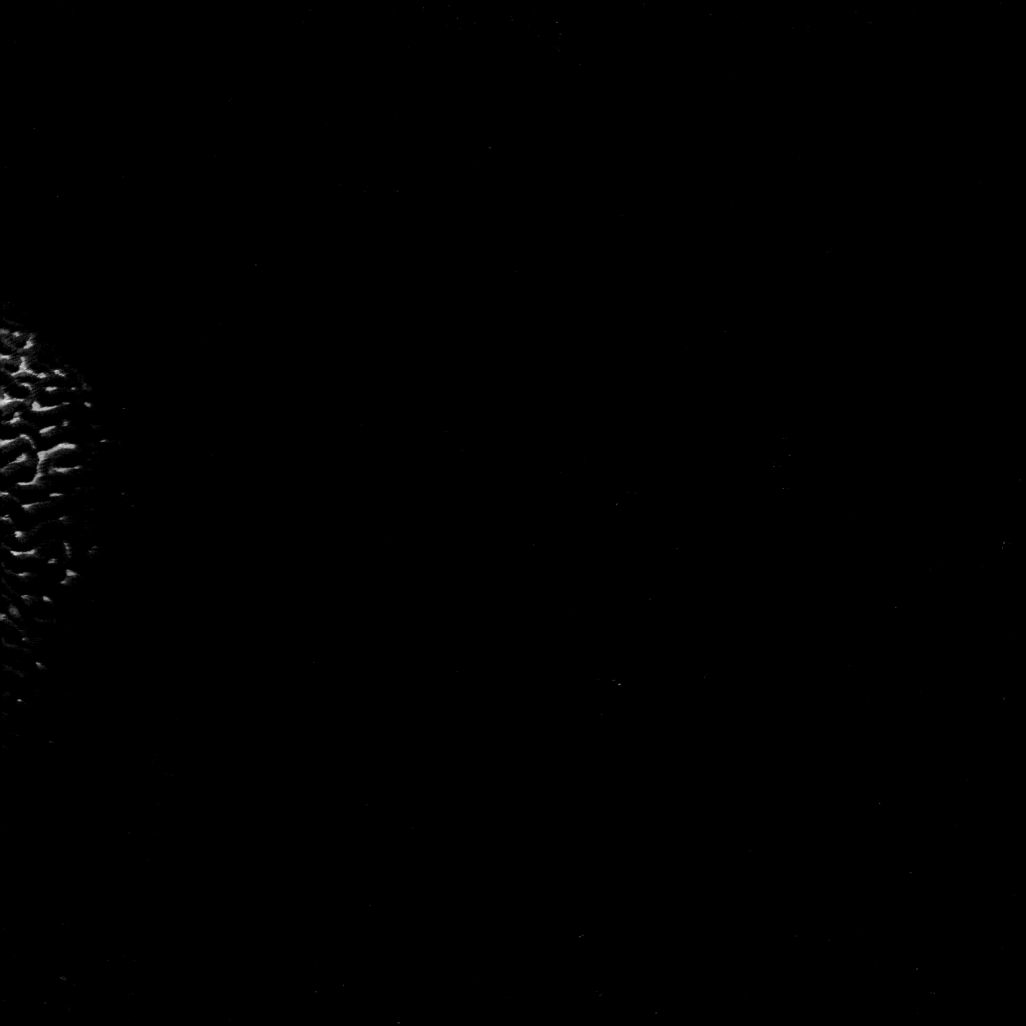

A single jewel anemone
floats freely in the seas
off Land's End, UK
Charles Hood

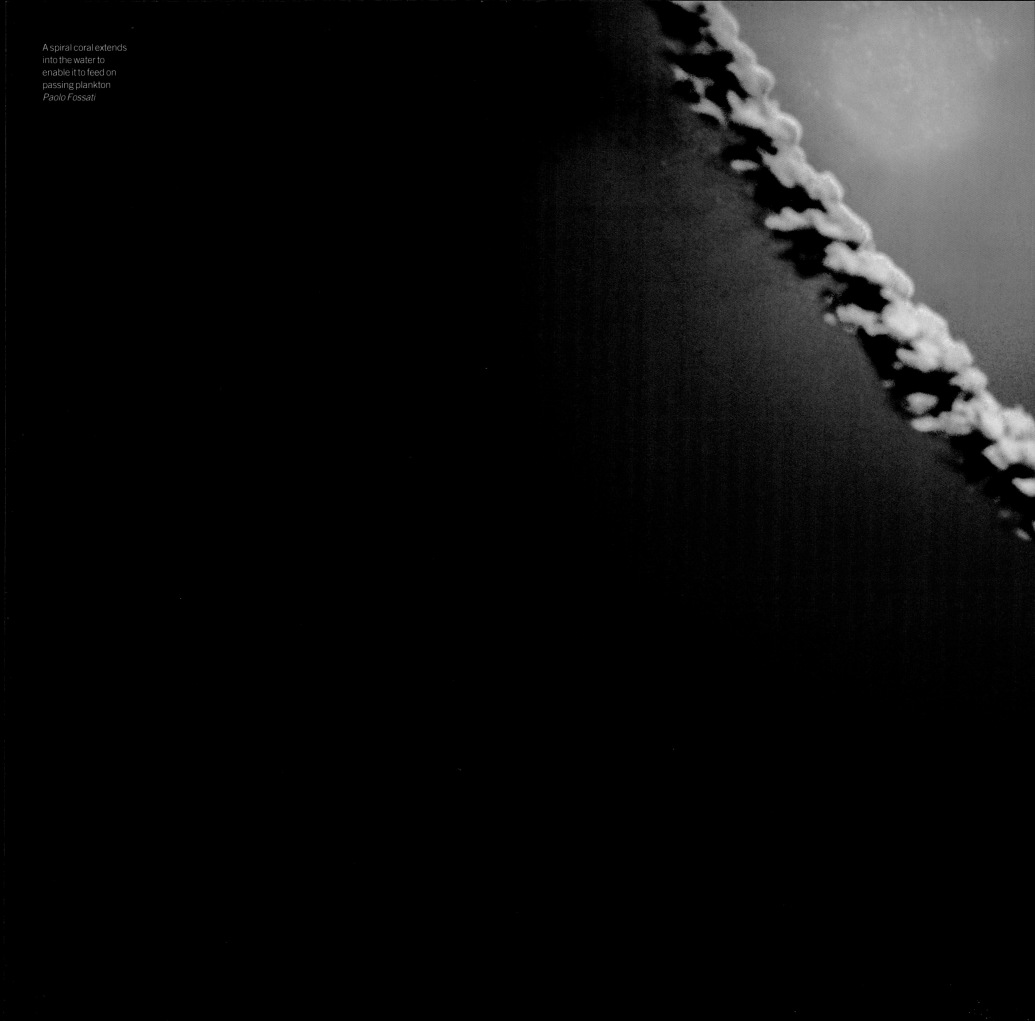

A spiral coral extends
into the water to
enable it to feed on
passing plankton
Paolo Fossati

Despite the fact that the
grey reef sharks are in
a feeding frenzy, the
smaller fish – remoras –
will remain safe
Ron and Valerie Taylor

Left A mosaic moray eel waits patiently for its unsuspecting prey
David Hall

Right Despite its fierce appearance, this moray is only 'smelling' the water in search of prey
Sergio Hanquet

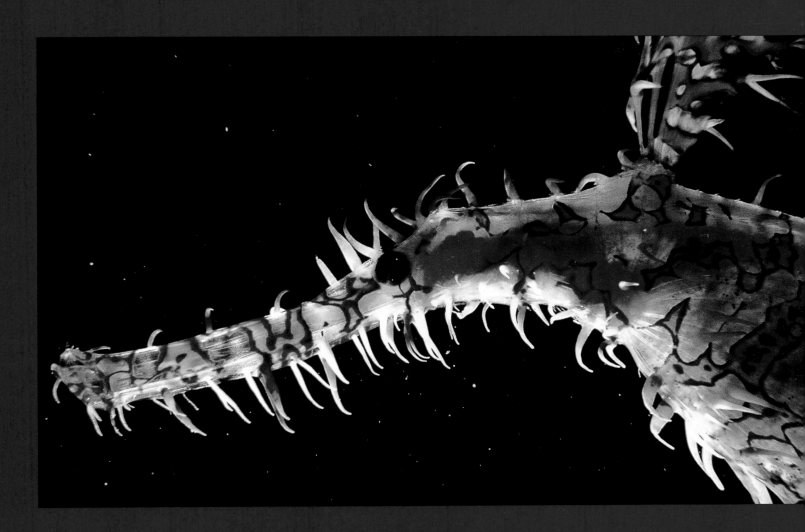

A rare sighting of a lone bottlenose dolphin – they usually travel in pods, courtesy of Great Barrier Reef Marine Park
Gordon Bull

Jean-Michel Cousteau

While the various species of fish and crustaceans make up the bulk of the population of the oceans, the largest inhabitants of this watery world are, in fact, mammals. Recently, scientists have begun to ask some fascinating questions about the cetaceans – and have made some equally fascinating discoveries in response to those questions. As each answer comes to light, the difference between humanity and the rest of the animal kingdom narrows to an ever-tighter margin and raises issues about the uniqueness of human intelligence

An extremely rare white
southern right whale
Brandon D Cole

months, they have to arrive early. Bowheads are one of the first animals to find their way into the leads as the ice breaks up. During summer, copepods, tiny crustaceans that swarm in their millions, can be found nearer the surface, and bowheads open their cavernous mouths to scoop them up. These whales have fine baleen plates that filter the copepods from the water.

For some species, timing is critical. Penguins arriving too late on their return to the Antarctic continent may be able to get to their rookeries, but they will not have time to rear and fledge their chicks. But if they arrive too early they might find their rookery inaccessible because of sea ice or snow cover. Conditions vary from year to year, with some disastrous results, but on average the migrants get it just right. In summer there is such a bounty of food that many species return year after year. Blue whales, fin, minke, humpbacks and southern right whales all travel thousands of miles to feed in the rich waters of the Southern Ocean.

The Southern Ocean that surrounds Antarctica is without doubt the roughest ocean in the world, enduring constant winds that blow uninterrupted around the continent. But it is a hospitable, easy place to live compared to the continent itself. The ocean is cold, so it is very rich in oxygen, and its nutrients are constantly mixed by turbulent currents; and so, in summer, when there is enough light, microscopic plants suspended in the surface waters grow and reproduce to form extensive blooms. Driven as it is by the vagaries of ocean upwellings and currents, the distribution of nutrients is very patchy and thus the resulting phytoplankton blooms are similarly random.

Animals graze on plants, and in Antarctica the most prolific of these are krill, or 'whale food' in Norwegian. Krill are the keystone of the Antarctic food chain, and they occur in huge swarms that can turn the ocean red. It is very easy to go to Antarctica and not even see an individual krill, partly because by day they stay deep, but also because

their distribution tends to mirror that of the phytoplankton blooms and is patchy. But do not be deceived. Krill are extremely numerous – an estimated 600 million million of them live in the Southern Ocean.

With such a vast source of protein it is not surprising that most animals in the Southern Ocean depend on krill as their basic food. Many whales, seals, fish, penguins and other seabirds hunt krill. Their methods vary from straining krill from giant mouthfuls of water using baleen plates, as the great baleen whales do, to picking out individual krill from the surface, in the manner of terns and other sea birds.

Before commercial whaling started in the Southern Ocean whales were abundant. But, with the depletion of whale populations, other krill-eating animals, such as crabeater seals, fur seals and penguins, have been able to take advantage of the lack of competition. It is possible that numbers of these species have risen significantly, and whales, some of which are making a steady comeback, face increased competition.

But competition now also comes from man. As well as fishing for squid and fish in the Southern Ocean, modern fisheries take krill. This raises an important conservation issue, for a misjudgment in the quota for krill would have serious implications throughout the Southern Ocean ecosystem. In 1990 all the countries that are signatory to the Antarctic Treaty agreed on a conservation strategy. This is a holistic approach to conservation, which takes into account the importance of one species to another. In effect, the catch levels for krill and other targeted species are now based not only on maintaining the population of that species, but also on minimising the impact on dependent species.

This is certainly a step forward in marine management. But what it does require is a complete understanding and careful monitoring of the ecosystem in question. Until we have that thorough knowledge we should be cautious about harvesting animals from such a unique and precious place.

The remainder of what
was once a massive
iceberg, courtesy of
Robert Harding Picture
Library, Minden Pictures
Frans Lanting

Left Slabs of ice
can sheer off an
iceberg, forming
precipitous sides
Martha Holmes

Right As the weather
warms, even giant
icebergs melt a little
Charles Tyler

Elephant seals bask in the sunshine of the brief Arctic summer
Charles Tyler

The massive majesty
of an elephant seal bull
Charles Tyler

The ocean is now a global theatre for sporting conquest – the start of the Sydney to Southport ocean yacht race
Ian Mainsbridge

The *Sohar*, the Omani
ship that was built to
recreate the voyages
of Sinbad the sailor
Richard Greenhill

The *Statraad Lehmkul*, a tall ship, sailing off the coast of Brittany, courtesy of *Robert Harding* Picture Library, Visa Image *Jean Guichard*

The modern-day
Argo, a replica of a
Bronze Age galley
Kevin Fleming

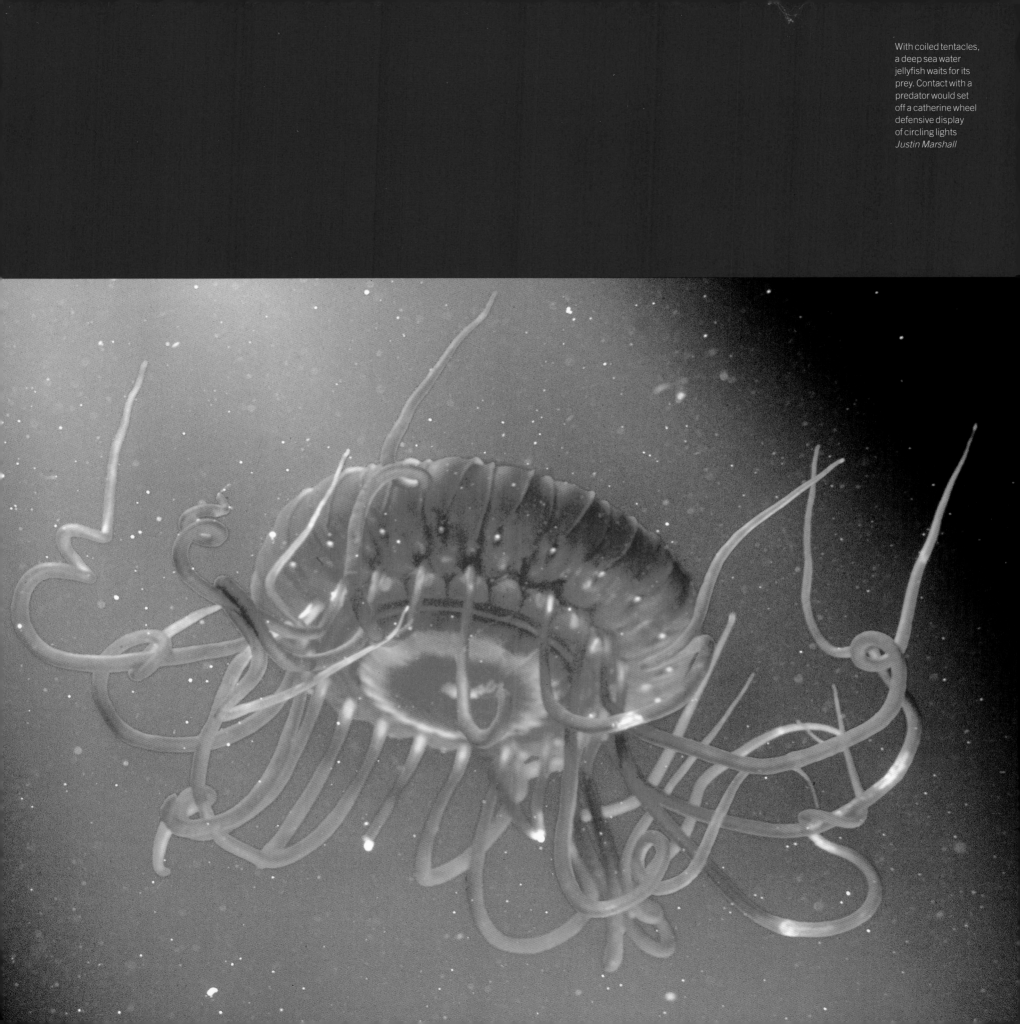

With coiled tentacles, a deep sea water jellyfish waits for its prey. Contact with a predator would set off a catherine wheel defensive display of circling lights
Justin Marshall

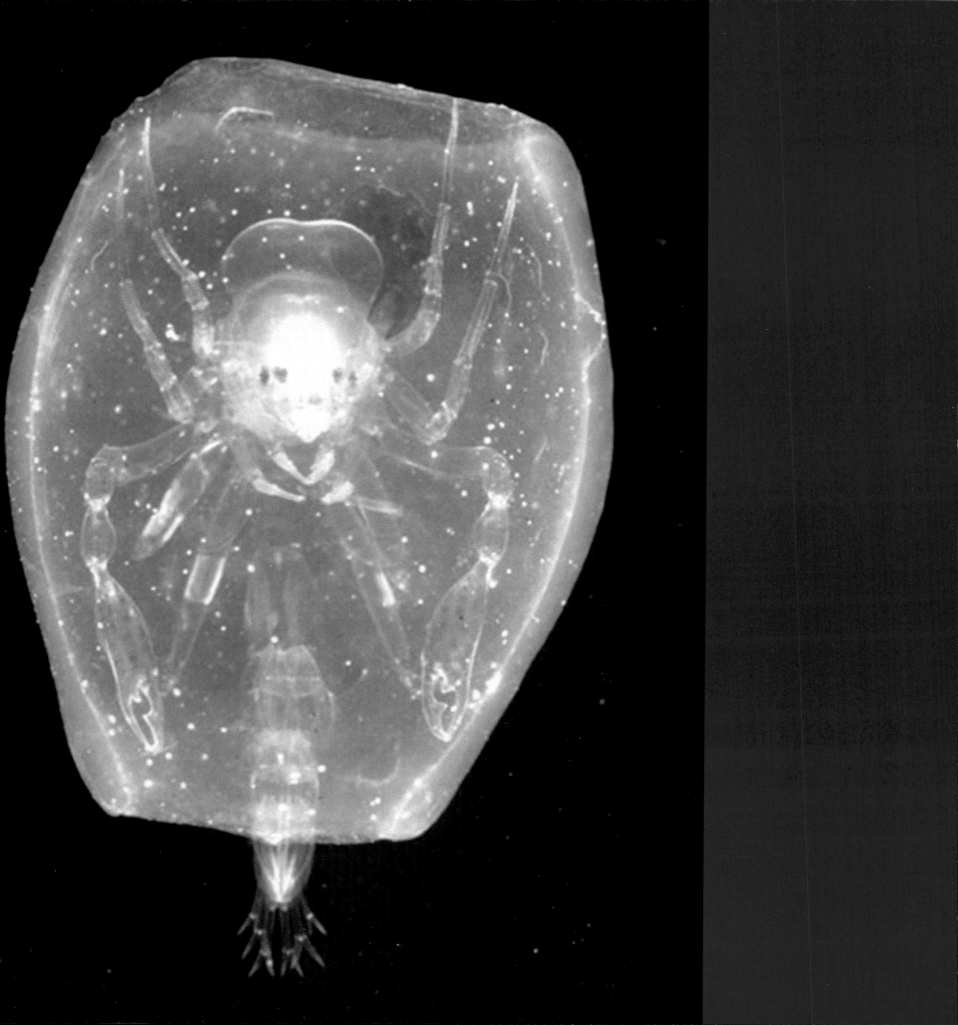

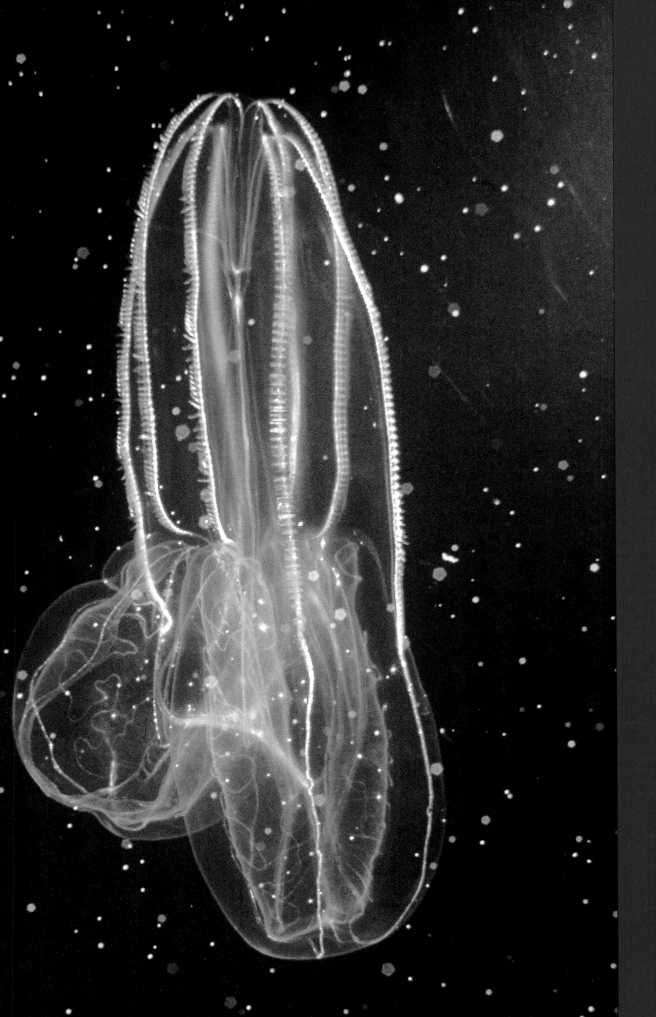